Road Rob

by Joy Cowley

The Road Robber was a giant
who stole roads.
He rolled them up like carpets
and took them away.

The Road Robber
cut up the roads and sold them
for tennis courts and skating rinks.

He made so much money,
he had his own big jet plane.

Now,
there was a beautiful road
called Strawberry Road
that went over the hill
and down to the town.

It had houses and gardens by it,
and people and bicycles
and cars on it.

Strawberry Road
was always full of smiles.

But one night,
that wicked Road Robber
stole beautiful Strawberry Road.

He rolled it up
and put it on his back.

Then, laughing, he ran away.

In the morning
the people cried,
"Look! Our road is gone!
How will we ride our bicycles?
How will we drive our cars?
How will we ever get to town?"

A little boy said,
"It's that wicked Road Robber!
Here are his footprints.
If we find the Road Robber,
we'll find our road."

So all the people
followed the big footprints.

Over the hill they went,
over a farm and over a river.

They came to the airstrip
where the Road Robber
had his big jet plane.

"I've seen that airstrip somewhere,"
said the little boy.
"That airstrip is our Strawberry Road."

"So it is!" cried the people.

The people waited
until the plane had taken off.

Then, quickly,
they rolled up Strawberry Road
and took it back home.

They rolled the road out flat
and nailed it down
so it couldn't be stolen again.

Once more,
Strawberry Road was full of smiles.

As for the wicked Road Robber,
he had to land in the sea.

Served him right!